Page04
RIC FLAIR
VS
MVP
CHRIS JERICHO
VS
JBL
Page18
REY MYSTERIO
VS
EDGE
Page30
DON
TONY
JERICHO

RIC FLAIR

During the first edition of *SmackDown* in 2008, MVP made the bold claim that he would force Ric Flair to retire. The United States Champion would get his opportunity to fulfil his lofty ambition at the *Royal Rumble*. Flair would once again be fighting for his sports-entertainment life, as the contest would be a Career Threatening Match for 'Naitch'.

MVP has vowed to end the career of 'Naitch' when they square off, and now he has to prove he's not all talk. Flair, however, has no intention of going quietly. The 'Dirtiest Player in the Game' has shown in recent weeks that he still has some tricks up his sleeve, and he will do anything to prolong his illustrious career.

But for Ric Flair to keep his livelihood, not only will he have to contend with one of WWE's toughest competitors, but also a

MVP

man who has beaten the 16-time World Champion before. At *Vengeance: Night of Champions* in June 2007, MVP stole a victory, and a page from Flair's book, when he low-blowed his way to the win.

Will Ric Flair be able to keep his career going at the *Royal Rumble* in another Career Threatening Match? Or will the brazen United States Champion, MVP, bring his list of accolades to even greater heights by retiring Flair?

"Well, here we are at historic Madison Square Garden to see the 21st annual Royal Rumble, and, I for one, can't wait to see this first match!"
"First up, we have Ric Flair who is going to take on the United States Champion, MVP!"
"I think just about everyone in this arena knows that this could be Ric Flair's last match since Mr McMahon declared that the next match Flair loses will be his last!"
"Ric Flair has had a career spanning over 35 years. To think that this could be his final match is simply astonishing."
"But you can bet that the cocky young MVP would love to be the man to end Flair's historic career."
"I bet some of the fans in attendance here tonight saw Flair's first match at Madison Square Garden way back in the 1970s!"
"There is no doubt about it, Cole. The fans really do love the 'Nature Boy'!"
Nature Boy

WRESTLEMANIA
"And I think it is pretty obvious that Flair feels the same about his fans here tonight!"
"Flair has been stylin' and profilin' since 1972, and is truly a legend."
"No one carries themselves quite like Flair. Just look at the man!"
"Those robes cost over $10,000 each, and how many have we seen over the years?"
"Ric Flair truly is 'The Man'!"

"There you see Ric Flair addressing the crowd here tonight. He knows that this could be his last match in MSG!"
"And he is obviously feeling quite emotional about that possibility."
"Flair has always said 'To be the man, you got to beat the man!' Tonight, *SmackDown's* Montel Vontavious Porter will try to do just that!"
"But you have to think, Flair will give everything he has to keep his career alive. There is no way he is going to just roll over tonight and let MVP score the victory. That said, MVP is one of the fastest-rising Superstars in WWE and I think he may just pull it off!"

"Well, Coach. We will soon get to see. Here comes the United States Champion, MVP."
"You're right, Coach. MVP has proven himself to be a force to be reckoned with here in WWE. Just look at what he did to Matt Hardy a few months back!"
"MVP is the longest-reigning United States Champion in the history of *SmackDown*. He is certainly no rookie."
"MVP sure does have a mean streak. He is also not afraid to bend the rules to ensure a victory."
"And just look at that! Look at the arrogance on display by MVP."
"MVP is a big-time player. He won't be intimidated by the occasion or his opponent!"

"Well the match is under way, and I think referee Charles Robinson is going to have a tough time tonight. Both of these guys have been known to break the rules in the past."
"It looks like a tentative start to this match, both men are feeling each other out. Neither wants to give up the advantage."
"But look at that, Coach! A huge chop from Ric Flair to the United States Champion! No one can hit a chop like the 'Nature Boy'!"
"Well, I think it is pretty obvious who you are rooting for here, Cole!"
"I'll make no excuses. I have a great deal of respect for Ric Flair and all he's done in his career. I think it would be a travesty if he lost tonight!"

"MVP whips Flair into the ropes and follows up with a huge boot to the face! I think that may have knocked Ric Flair clean out!"
"That was simply devastating from MVP. He sure seems to be pumped up for this match!"
"MVP is going for the pin! 1...2...Flair just managed to kick out. Come on, Ric!"
"You see, that is the difference between you and me, Cole. I am professional enough to remain impartial, where as you scream like a little girl for your favourites!"

"I have to disagree with you there, Coach. Anyway, MVP is working over Ric Flair with an armbar!"
"MVP has that move locked in real tight. I'm not sure Flair will be able to escape this!"
"Flair is making his way back up to his feet!"
"But check this out, Cole! MVP with a hard Irish Whip into the corner!"
"Flair bounces back off the turnbuckle into the path of the waiting MVP, who delivers a huge back-body drop!"
PROTECT THIS

"MVP whips Flair into the opposite corner, and what can he be planning here?"
"MVP is looking for something big here. He is building up a head of steam, and comes storming across the ring to deliver a huge boot to the face of Flair."
"Flair must be out of it, Coach!"
"And would you look at that! Charles Robinson is arguing with MVP in an obvious attempt to buy Flair some time."
"It is no secret that Charles Robinson and Ric Flair are great friends. Back in WCW, they were even tag team partners for a short time."
"They even called Robinson 'Little Naitch'. In my opinion, Charles Robinson is biased and should not be allowed to referee this match!"
PROTECT THIS RING

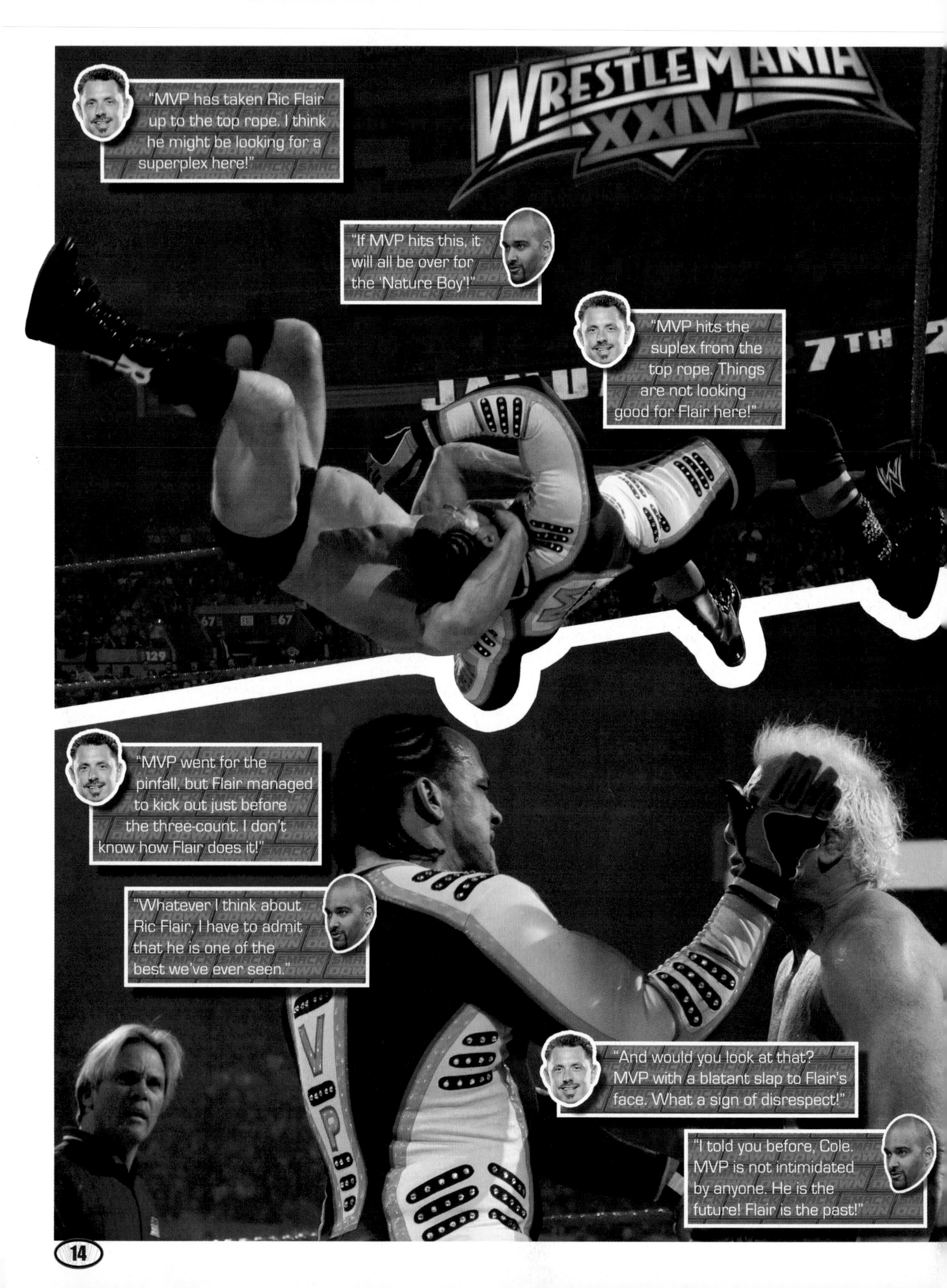
WRESTLEMANIA XXIV
"MVP has taken Ric Flair up to the top rope. I think he might be looking for a superplex here!"
"If MVP hits this, it will all be over for the 'Nature Boy'!"
"MVP hits the suplex from the top rope. Things are not looking good for Flair here!"
"MVP went for the pinfall, but Flair managed to kick out just before the three-count. I don't know how Flair does it!"
"Whatever I think about Ric Flair, I have to admit that he is one of the best we've ever seen."
"And would you look at that? MVP with a blatant slap to Flair's face. What a sign of disrespect!"
"I told you before, Cole. MVP is not intimidated by anyone. He is the future! Flair is the past!"

"MVP has Flair up on his back and he may be looking for a Samoan Drop here, Coach."
"MVP is an all-around athlete. He has the speed, the agility and the strength!"
"But look at that! Flair managed to wiggle his way out of it!"
"Flair delivers a huge chop to the champion's chest, and you know that has to hurt!"
"I have been on the receiving end of that move before, and believe me, MVP will be feeling that for a week!"

"Wait though, Coach! It looks like MVP is going for the Playmaker! If he hits it, it will be the end for Ric Flair!"
"This is a devastating move. No one gets up after being hit with it!"
PROTECT THIS
"Hold on a second! Flair has reversed the move. He is going for his patented Figure-Four Leglock! Can Flair lock it in?"
"MVP is battling hard to keep Ric Flair from applying this maneuvre. Don't let him get it locked in, MVP!"

"Flair almost has it locked in. The end could be near for MVP!"
"MVP will never quit! He is way too tough for that!"
"Flair just needs to lean back and apply the pressure and this match will be over!"
PROTECT THIS RING
"Flair has it locked in! MVP just might have to tap!"
"Don't do it, MVP! Don't do it!"
"MVP taps! MVP taps! Ric Flair has won it! Flair lives on to fight another day!"
WRESTLEMANIA XXIV
"I don't believe it! MVP looked like he was going to win this! He was all over Flair all the way through the match!"
"Ric Flair used his experience to overcome the younger competitor here tonight. All it took was one little mistake from MVP and Flair seized the opportunity to lock on the Figure Four and force the United States Champion to tap out! What a match!"

CHRIS JERICHO

On the surface, Chris Jericho and John 'Bradshaw' Layfield are polar opposites. One is a beloved champion of the people who wants to 'save us'; the other is a self-proclaimed 'Wrestling God' who demands that our fans and everyone else in WWE worship him. But these two are history-making champions who want the same thing – to be atop the mountain in WWE again. That's just one reason their mutual hatred will boil over when they meet for the first time ever at *Royal Rumble*.

Royal Rumble marks the in-ring return of JBL, who was forced to retire in 2006 following a loss to Rey Mysterio. The arrogant, self-made millionaire, whose 10-month WWE Championship reign between 2004 and 2005 was the longest in the previous 10 years, seems more intense than ever and hell-bent on proving a point at Y2J's expense. But has the former WWE Champion picked on the wrong man to make his statement?

Like JBL, Jericho knows something about being forced to leave. In 2005, he was fired after losing to John Cena in a 'You're Fired' Match. During his two years away, Y2J pursued other interests in Hollywood

oured with his band Fozzy, hosted his wn radio show and wrote a best-selling utobiography, *A Lion's Tale: Around the World in Spandex*. But most of all, the irst-ever Undisputed WWE Champion ested, watched and waited for the right ime to return. And when he returned n November, he was determined not to lwell on his past, but make history again.

Will Jericho get revenge on JBL for costing him the WWE Championship and save us rom the 'Wrestling God's' comeback? Or will JBL show that Jericho cannot even save himself from his divine wrath?

"And here we go with our second match of the evening! The recently returned Chris Jericho will be taking on the also returning John 'Bradshaw' Layfield."
"I have been looking forward to the return of JBL for months. He was one of the most dominant WWE Champions of all time, and a pretty good commentator to boot."
BREAK
"I have to admit that it does feel kind of strange seeing JBL in the ring after having him sit next to me for so long on *SmackDown*. Still, I think he is really going to have his work cut out for him tonight!"
Y2J
"Chris Jericho was the first man to hold the Undisputed WWE Championship. He is certainly no slouch! Add to that the mind games JBL has been playing over the past few weeks and you know, Jericho is going to pumped up for this one!"

"JBL has been itching to get back into the ring. I don't know why he dislikes Chris Jericho so much, but he certainly looks focused tonight!"
"And here comes the 'Wrestling God'!, JBL. Man, he looks in great shape for someone who has been out of the game for so long."
"Like you said, Coach, JBL held the WWE Championship for 280 days. He is also a former United States, Hardcore, European and World Tag Team Champion."
"He is actually a former 17-time Hardcore Champion. That has to prove that JBL is not scared of a fight!"
"I am pretty sure JBL has never been intimidated in his life!"

"One thing that JBL will never be is popular with this crowd! It is pretty clear that this New York crowd doesn't care for the Wall Street analyst!"
"Perhaps JBL gave out some bad financial advice! Or perhaps it is his complete disregard for the rules of the match!"
"JBL is not a rule breaker! He just does what it takes to win!"
"The referee is explaining the rules to the two participants, although I don't know how much they are listening. Both men look like they want to rip each other apart!"
"Well after the comments JBL made last week on *Raw*, this match could be the most emotionally charged of the night!"

"After JBL ruined Jericho's chance at winning the WWE Championship at *Armageddon* just a month ago, Y2J has been gunning for JBL every opportunity he gets."
"Jericho has been waiting for this opportunity for weeks now, and tonight he has his chance to get his revenge."
"JBL really stepped over the line when he spoke about Jericho's family on *Raw*."
"And who can forget JBL wrapping that camera cable around the neck of Y2J? Jericho is still carrying the injury he sustained at the hands of that vicious attack, and a bruised larynx is like a red rag to a bull. You can bet JBL is going to target that area!"
Y2J

"The match is under way, and Jericho hits JBL with a huge flying forearm that sends JBL crashing to the mat."
"Jericho really caught him with that one! JBL may be knocked out cold!"
"And look at this, Coach! Chris Jericho is going for the Walls of Jericho! Oh my god! He has it locked in! The match could be over right here!"
"I think Jericho has gone for this move too early. JBL has made it to the ropes, and the referee forces Jericho to break the hold."
"Jericho looks to be in complete control thus far! JBL has rolled to the outside of the ring!"
"I am not sure what JBL is looking for on the outside. Hey! Here comes Jericho with a baseball slide to the outside!"
"Jericho sends JBL crashing face first into the Spanish announce table! What an incredible move!"

"Both men are back in the ring! Jericho sends JBL into the ropes, but JBL comes back with a devastating clothesline."
"That clothesline almost took Jericho's head off! JBL is back in control."
"JBL is blatantly choking Chris Jericho on the bottom rope, right in front of the referee! That sure isn't going to help Jericho's bruised larynx."
"JBL is well within his rights to do that, as long as he breaks the hold before the referee's count of five!"
"That may be true, Coach, but it sure isn't going to win JBL any fans here tonight!"

"JBL has Jericho set up for the slingshot maneuvre under the middle rope! This could be really bad for Y2J!"
"JBL has picked a body part and now he is going to work on it. The injured throat of Chris Jericho puts him at a distinct disadvantage. It really is a smart tactic by JBL!"
"JBL pulls Jericho back to his feet and locks in a sleeper hold. This move cuts off the flow of blood to your brain and can send you to sleep in a matter of seconds."
"Not only that, Cole! This will apply even more pressure to Jericho's throat!"

"JBL is gradually wearing down Chris Jericho with the sleeper. Jericho really needs to get back to a vertical base here, or else the match may be over!"
"JBL is such a smart guy. His tactics are working so well here, and he looks like he is in complete control here!"
"Don't speak too soon, Coach! Jericho is back on his feet! JBL sends Jericho into the ropes and is looking for the big boot to the face!"
"But look, Cole! Jericho ducked under JBL's massive boot and is looking for some offense of his own!"

"Chris Jericho comes flying across the ring a delivers a thunderous clothesline that takes JBL down!"
"I don't know how Jericho is still in this match! He looked as though he was a beaten man!"
"Jericho has the heart of a lion, that's for sure!"
"Jericho may be looking for another clothesline here! But, oh no! JBL catches him with a huge boot to the face which sends Jericho crashing to the canvas!"
"JBL is back in control here, and I can't see any way that Jericho can come back from a move like that!"
Y2J
JERICHO

"JBL takes Jericho by the neck and sends him face first into the ringpost!"
"This is more like the JBL I remember! Smash-mouth and in your face!"
"Jericho is back to his feet though, Coach!"
"Not for long, Cole! While the referee had his back turned, JBL hit Jericho with a low blow!"
"Jericho can't lose the match like this!"
"JBL sends Jericho into the ropes once more and again catches him with a huge kick to the jaw!"
"JBL goes for the pin! 1...2...3! JBL has won it!"
"JBL has defeated Chris Jericho here at the *Royal Rumble*! Jericho is going to feel rightly cheated out of a victory here tonight!"
"It may not have been pretty, but JBL got the job done!"

REY MYSTERIO

After winning the Beat the Clock challenge on *SmackDown*, the high-flying Rey Mysterio will challenge Edge for his World Heavyweight Championship at *Royal Rumble*.

While Rey will be looking to recapture the gold he once held, the 'Rated-R Superstar' has no intention of letting his title go, and he has the backing of *SmackDown's* General Manager, Vickie Guerrero.

Mysterio will attempt to regain the title with an advantage few competitors have against Edge: familiarity.

In 2002, Edge & Rey were WWE Tag Team Champions together and they know each other both in the ring and out. Mysterio also is very familiar with Edge's ace in the hole, Vickie Guerrero. The GM was instrumental in Rey's knee being demolished when she betrayed the

longtime Guerrero family friend to aid Chavo Guerrero in their 2006 rivalry. Will the high-flying Mysterio find a way to overcome the odds to carry the gold once more? Or will the 'Ultimate Opportunist', along with his friends Curt Hawkins, Zack Ryder and Vickie keep the title around Edge's waist?

"Well, here we go with the main event of the evening. World Heavyweight Champion Edge is set to take on the No 1 contender, Rey Mysterio!"
"This is going to be one hell of a match! And here comes the champ!"
"Edge was defeated by Mysterio on *SmackDown* just a few weeks ago in the Beat the Clock Challenge, thus earning Mysterio his title shot tonight."
"Edge doesn't need to be thinking about that loss though, Cole. And looking at him tonight, he looks super-confident!"
EDGE

"But what the hell is this? SmackDown general manager Vickie Guerrero is making her way to ringside with the help of her assistant, Theodore Long!"
"Vickie Guerrero has every right to be here. Her and Edge are in a relationship and she is simply here to support her man!"
"Vickie Guerrero has been confined to a wheelchair since taking that Chokeslam from Undertaker several weeks ago!"
"And what a despicable act that was on Undertaker's part! Beating on a poor, defenceless woman!"
"Well, if you remember, Vickie did get herself involved in the match between Edge and Undertaker. Besides, Edge let it happen. He could have stopped the attack had he not been such a coward!"
"Well, at least tonight, Vickie will have Hawkins and Ryder to take care of her!"
"Yes, but does that not give Edge an unfair advantage, having his buddies on the outside of the ring?"

"Like I said, the 'Edgeheads' are here only to offer protection to Vickie Guerrero. I am sure that they have no intention of becoming involved in the match!"
"Well, I guess only time will tell!"
"And here comes the challenger, the electrifying Rey Mysterio!"
"I don't know where Mysterio gets all those bizarre masks from, Cole?"
"Mysterio prides himself on celebrating his Mexican heritage and the Lucha Libre-style masks are a huge part of his history! Besides, I think he looks great!"

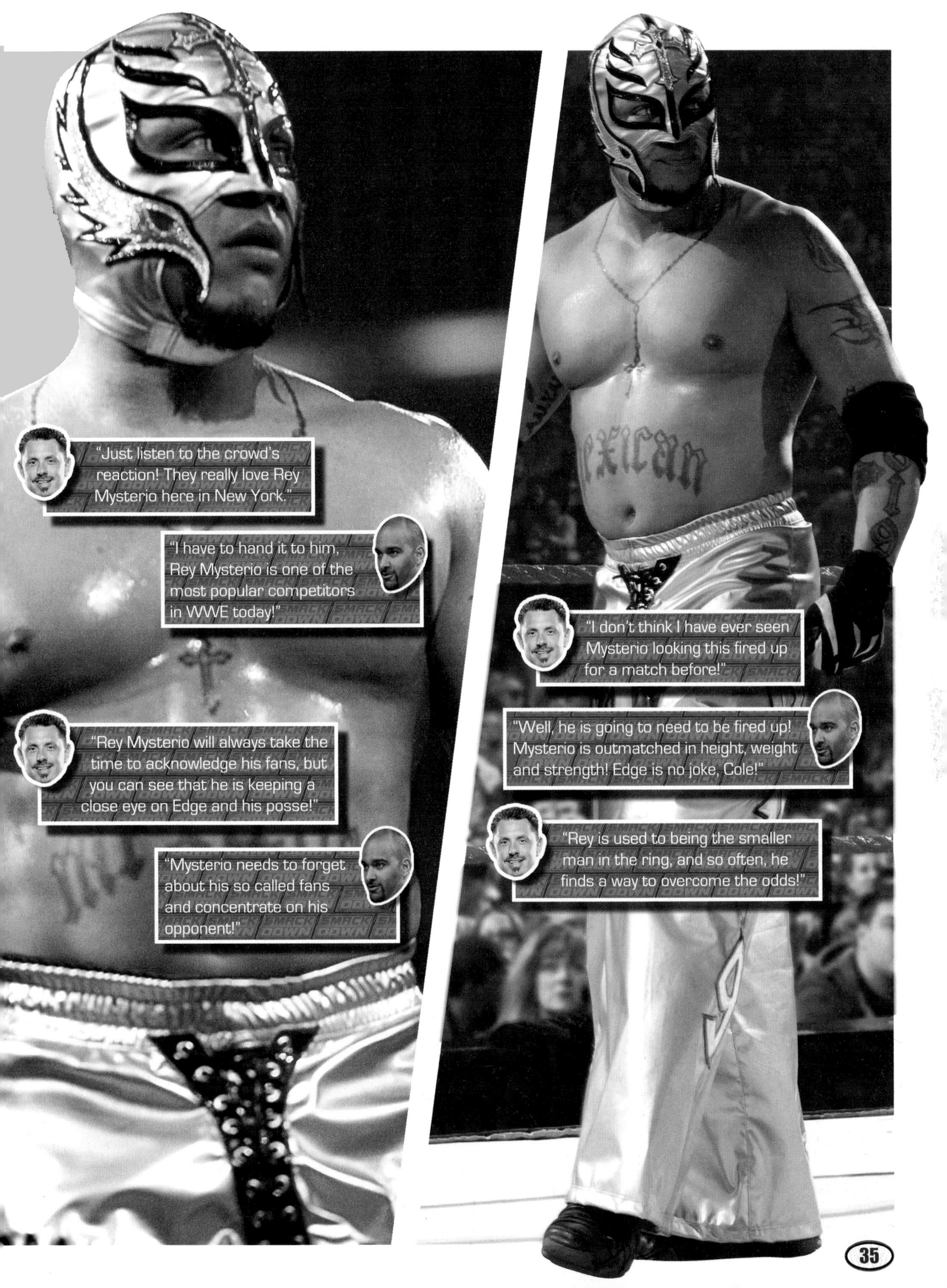
"Just listen to the crowd's reaction! They really love Rey Mysterio here in New York."
"I have to hand it to him, Rey Mysterio is one of the most popular competitors in WWE today!"
"Rey Mysterio will always take the time to acknowledge his fans, but you can see that he is keeping a close eye on Edge and his posse!"
"Mysterio needs to forget about his so called fans and concentrate on his opponent!"
"I don't think I have ever seen Mysterio looking this fired up for a match before!"
"Well, he is going to need to be fired up! Mysterio is outmatched in height, weight and strength! Edge is no joke, Cole!"
"Rey is used to being the smaller man in the ring, and so often, he finds a way to overcome the odds!"

"Just look at the World Heavyweight Champion, Edge! There is no way that Mysterio is going to be able to defeat him."
"I will admit that Edge has been pretty dominant since capturing the title, But Rey has beaten Edge several times before and the two of them know each other so well. They were even WWE Tag Team champions together at one point."
"The match is under way, and immediately, Edge uses his strength to overpower Mysterio."
"Edge has Mysterio in a side headlock. This will start to wear down his opponent."
619

"Edge seems to be looking for some kind of ankle or knee lock. It is no secret that Rey Mysterio has a weak knee. In fact, he returned not long ago from major knee surgery."
"Edge is really smart. He knows what Rey's weakness is and is going to exploit it."
"Edge has Mysterio locked in a single-leg Boston Crab. This is really going to take its toll on Mysterio."
"If you can take out Mysterio's legs, you take away all of his high-flying offense!"
"Edge is really leaning back, applying more pressure to both Mysterio's knee and lower back."
"Mysterio needs to escape this move quickly if he is going to have any chance in this matchup!"

"Rey is slowly making his way back up to his feet, but Edge is doing his best to force him back down to the canvas."
"Rey is never going to win a test of strength against Edge!"
"Rey is really feeding off the crowd here! He is back to his feet!"
"How on earth did he do that, Cole?"
"Rey fires off the ropes and catches Edge with a picture-perfect Bulldog!"
"Edge is down and out after having his face driven into the mat!"

"Mysterio has climbed to the top rope! What can he be thinking here?"
"Edge is still out of it on the mat below!"
"Rey Mysterio flies from the top rope looking to land the double stomp on his opponent!"
"Get out of the way, Edge!"
"Rey Mysterio lands with all his weight across the chest of the World Heavyweight Champion, Edge!"
"That obviously hurt Edge and he has done the right thing in rolling out of the ring to buy himself a little time."

"Edge isn't safe on the outside though, Coach. Look at Mysterio! Mysterio with a suicide dive over the top rope!"
"Both men are down, I think that hurt Mysterio as much as it did Edge!"
"Mysterio and Edge slowly make their way back into the ring. Edge is looking for that ankle lock again!"
"Edge has it locked in, in the centre of the ring! Mysterio may have to tap out!"

"Just look at the determination on the World Heavyweight Champion's face! Edge is trying to tear Rey Mysterio's knee apart!"
"There is absolutely no way that Mysterio can escape this hold!"
"Rey Mysterio is desperately trying to escape! He is trying to get back to his feet and force Edge to break the hold!"
"Mysterio escapes and hits Edge with an Enziguri that leaves the champion out on his back! I thought Edge had the win there, Cole!"

"Rey Mysterio has climbed up to the top rope! I'm not sure what he is thinking here!"
"Mysterio with the Frog Splash from the top! Shades of the late, great Eddie Guerrero there, Cole!"
"With Vickie Guerrero at ringside, Rey Mysterio may have just won the World Heavyweight Championship with his best friends old signature move!"
"Mysterio is going for the cover! The ref is counting! 1...2...Edge kicks out!"
"The match is not over yet! Edge has kicked out of the Frog Splash!"

"Mysterio has gone to the outside! It looks like he may be going for the West Coast Pop, Coach!"
"Mysterio flies through the air looking to hit his signature maneuvre on his opponent!"
"But look, Coach! Edge caught him with the Spear in mid air! Edge is going for the cover! 1...2...3! Edge retains the World Heavyweight Championship!"
"What an amazing move from Edge! That came out of nowhere!"
"I don't know how he did it, but Edge has managed to hold onto his title! Mysterio came so close!"
"Just look at how relieved Edge looks on the outside! Vickie is obviously proud of her man!"
"It sure was an incredible main event here at the *Royal Rumble*! Until next time, from Coach and me, Michael Cole, goodbye!"

ROYAL

"For 20 years, the Road to *WrestleMania* has begun with the *Royal Rumble* match, a 30-man over-the-top rope war where the winner earns an opportunity to face a World Champion on the grandest stage of them all. For that reason alone, a spot in the *Royal Rumble* match itself is one of the most coveted opportunities in sports-entertainment."

Jonathan Coachman

WHAT IS THE *ROYAL RUMBLE*® MATCH AND WHAT ARE ITS RULES?

HERE IS A REFRESHER COURSE:

- The object of the *Royal Rumble* match is to throw your opponent over the top rope. Both feet must touch the floor for their elimination to be official.
- The *Royal Rumble* features 30 Superstars of WWE from *Raw, SmackDown* and *ECW*.
- Two Superstars drawn at random start the match. New Superstars enter the Rumble every 90 seconds.
- The last man standing in the ring is the winner and gets an opportunity to challenge a World Champion in the main event at *WrestleMania*.
- The luck of the draw can be vital in the *Royal Rumble*. Superstars who randomly draw the first two spots in the match have much less of a chance of winning than the lucky soul who grabs No. 30. However, as some past winners have shown, drawing No. 1 is not a death knell to *WrestleMania* main event dreams.

MOST *RUMBLE* WINS

Stone Cold Steve Austin – 1997, 1998, 2001.

LONGEST TIME IN THE RING

Rey Mysterio has the longest recorded time in the *Royal Rumble* with a 1 hour, 2 minutes, 12 seconds stint in 2006. The shortest time in the ring for a winner was in 2001. Stone Cold Steve Austin became the *Royal Rumble* winner to spend the shortest amount of time in the match at nine minutes. In 2005, Batista came in a close second at roughly 10 minutes.

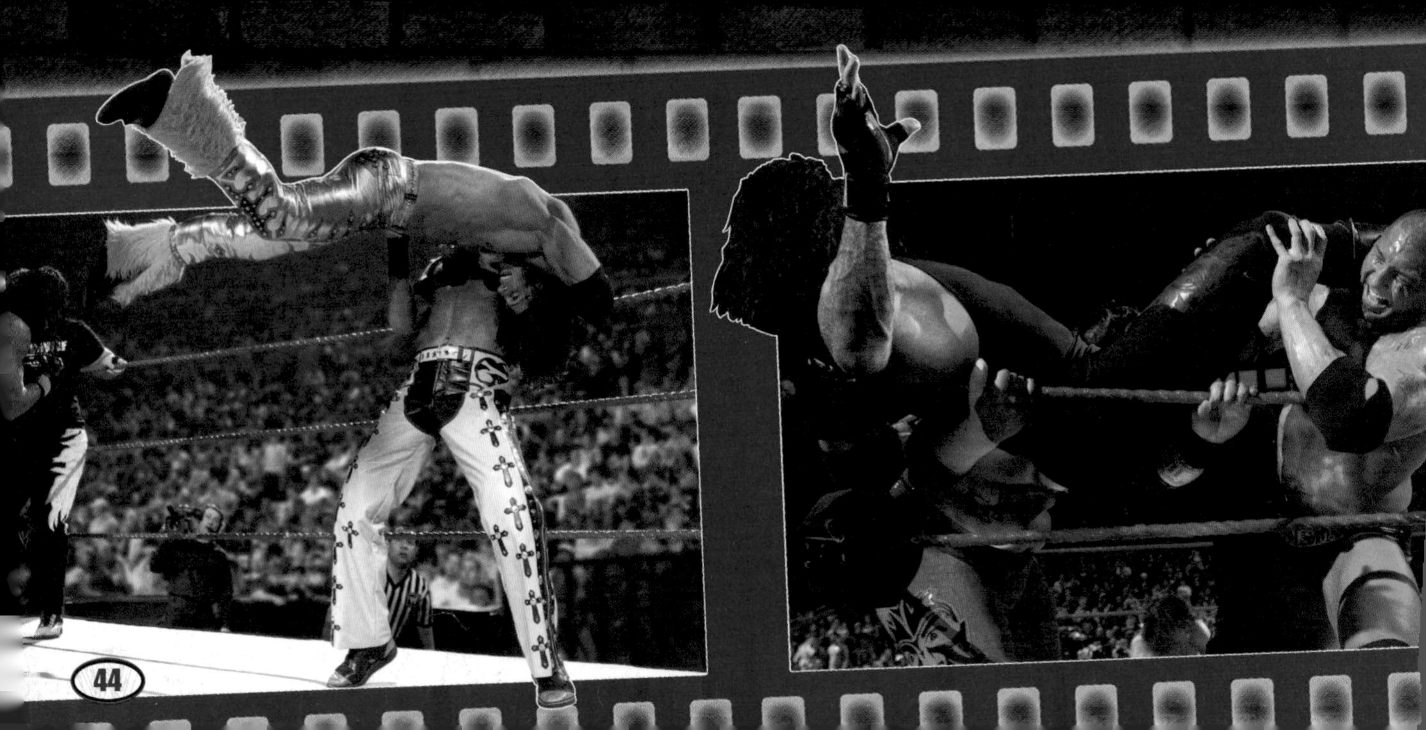

UMBLE® ...FACTS

NTRY NUMBER WITH THE MOST WINS

'he *Royal Rumble* entry number with the most wins is No. 27. Big John Studd (1989), Yokozuna (1993), Bret 'Hit Man' Hart (1994) and Stone Cold Steve Austin (2001) all entered with this very lucky number.

MOST OVERALL ELIMINATIONS

Stone Cold Steve Austin holds the record for most eliminations overall, having tossed 36 Superstars over the top rope.

MOST ELIMINATIONS IN A SINGLE *RUMBLE*

Kane eliminated 11 men in 2001: Grandmaster Sexay, Steve Blackman, Al Snow, Raven, Perry Saturn, Honky Tonk Man, Tazz, Crash Holly, Albert, Scotty 2 Hotty and The Rock.

CONSECUTIVE *RUMBLE* WINS

Three Superstars have won back-to-back *Rumbles*: Hulk Hogan (1990 & 1991), Shawn Michaels (1995 & 1996) and Stone Cold Steve Austin (1997 & 1998).

LONGEST *ROYAL RUMBLE®* MATCH

The 2002 *Royal Rumble* was the longest ever. It lasted 1 hour, 9 minutes, 23 seconds.

SHORTEST *ROYAL RUMBLE®* MATCH

The 1988 *Royal Rumble* was the shortest ever. It lasted 33 minutes. The match had only 20 Superstars, as opposed to 30.

SHORTEST *ROYAL RUMBLE®* WITH 30 ENTRANTS

The shortest *Royal Rumble* Match with 30 entrants took place in 1995. With participants entering in 60-second intervals, this match lasted a little more than 38 minutes.

WOMEN IN THE *RUMBLE* MATCH

In 1999, Chyna became the only woman in history to be an entrant in the *Royal Rumble* Match. She was eliminated by Stone Cold Steve Austin.

MOST CONSECUTIVE *RUMBLE* APPEARANCES

Kane has the most consecutive appearances in the *Rumble* with ten between 1999 and 2008.

SUPERSTARS WHO ELIMINATED THEMSELVES

Andre the Giant (1989), Drew Carey (2001), Kane (1999), Mick Foley (2004) & Faarooq (1997).

ROYAL
RE

KEY:

RAW ECW SMACKDOWN

	Wrestler	Match Entrance No	Match Elimination No
 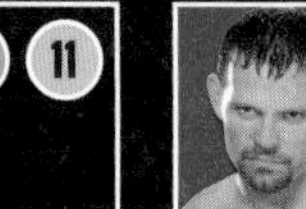	UNDERTAKER	1	11
 	SHAWN MICHAELS	2	12
 	SANTINO MARELLA	3	1
 	THE GREAT KHALI	4	2
 	HARDCORE HOLLY	5	6
 	JOHN MORRISON	6	14
 	TOMMY DREAMER	7	3
 	BATISTA	8	26
 	HORNSWOGGLE	9	?
 	CHUCK PALUMBO	10	5

	Wrestler	Match Entrance No	Match Elimination No
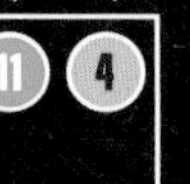	JAMIE NOBLE	11	4
	CM PUNK	12	15
	CODY RHODES	13	16
	UMAGA	14	24
 	GENE SNITSKY	15	10
	THE MIZ	16	13
 	SHELTON BENJAMIN	17	7
 	JIMMY SNUKA	18	9
	"ROWDY" RODDY PIPER	19	8
 	KANE	20	25

	Wrestler	Match Entrance No	Match Elimination No
	CARLITO	21	20
	MICK FOLEY	22	18
	MR KENNEDY	23	23
 	BIG DADDY V	24	17
	MARK HENRY	25	22
	CHAVO GUERRERO	26	21
 	ELIJAH BURKE	27	19
	TRIPLE H	28	27
	JOHN CENA	29	0